Letterland

Content

Fix-it Phonics

Notes to users

Teachers, supervisors and parents
At the bottom of each page you will find **teaching notes**. These notes provide explanation and information about the activities on each page so you are aware of the objectives.

Arrows ➤ | Instructions on how to complete an activity.

Lesson Structure
1. Start every Letterland lesson with the '**Hello**' song.
(See *Fix-it Phonics Starter Audio CD - Track 1* or Software)
2. Review previous learning with role play and/or circle time,
3. Introduce a new topic/letter sound and action. Complete as much as time allows.
4. End each lesson with the '**Good bye**' chant and song.
(See *Fix-it Phonics Starter Audio CD 2 - Track 2* or Software)

Sing ➤ | Listen to the song first. Then join in with just the '**hello**' and '**hi**'. Finally sing the whole song together!

Track 1
CD 2

Sing and move!

Hi, hello! Let's wave! Hello.

Hi, hello! Let's wave! Hello.

How are you?

I'm fine, thank you!

Hello, hello. Ok, let's go!

Let's go to Letterland! (x2)

Learning with music

Sing this song at the start of every Letterland session/lesson to reinforce how to say '**hello**' in a memorable, fun and inclusive way.

Circle time!

Use circle time at the start of each lesson to build confidence in reviewing the language taught previously.

Sing ➤ Listen to the song first, then join in with just the '**Good bye**'. As your class becomes more familiar with the song, join in more and more!

Track 2
CD 2

Sing and move!

Good bye, good bye.

See you soon.

Bye bye, bye bye.

See you soon.

It's been fun.

We'll see you soon.

Good bye, good bye from Letterland!

Multi-sensory

Sing this song at the end of every Letterland session/lesson to reinforce how to say '**good bye**'!

My classroom

Listen Listen to the names of the objects and point to them as you hear them. Then try saying the names of the objects.

Track 3
CD 2

Listen, point and say!

teacher

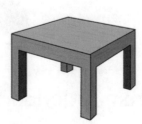

Speaking & listening

Use this new vocabulary as often as possible as you point to and use things in the classroom. Use your software to play another listening game.

Sing

Listen to the song first, then join in with pointing to the things in the scene. Finally sing the whole song together.

Track 4
CD 2

Sing and point!

This is a table.

This is a chair.

That is a window,

over there.

This is a pencil.

This is a pen.

That is a book.

Let's sing again.

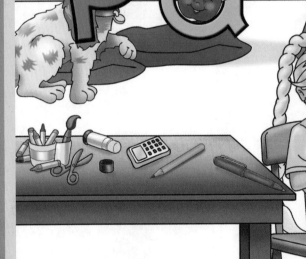

Software includes animated songs!

Multi-sensory

Children develop their communication skills and expand their vocabulary by listening and singing along to songs.

How many...? Listen and join the pictures to the correct numbers. Then try working in pairs to ask and answer the questions.

 Track 5 CD 2

Listen and match!

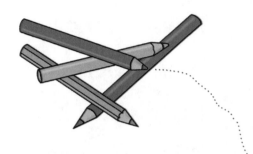

 Reinforce & review

This exercise combines the learning of new 'Classroom' words with reviewing knowledge of numbers.

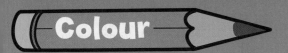

Do you have these things in your classroom?
Colour them to match yours.

door

pencil

book

pen

bag

Circle the odd one out in each row.

Find

Can you find six differences between these two pictures? Colour a star as you find each one.

tent

tree trunk

train

My family

Listen Listen to the words. Then listen as each syllable is clapped out in the word. You try clapping or drumming the syllables.

Track 6
CD 2

 Listen, drum or clap!

 mum

 dad

 sister

 brother

 grandma

 grandpa

 Syllable clapping Being able to identify syllables allows children to begin to associate spoken language with written words.

Sing ➡ Listen and join in with the actions and the song. If possible, each child can draw a picture or bring in a photo of their own family.

Track 7
CD 2

Software includes animated songs!

Sing and point!

Say hello to my family.
My mum and dad and me!
My brother and sister you can see.
This is my family and this is me!

Say hello to my family
That's grandma and grandpa you can see.
I love my family and my family loves me!
Say hello to my family. Say hello to my family.

Oral fluency Children develop their communication skills by listening and singing along to songs.

Can you find five **differences** between these two pictures?

 **Find**

Which family has two members that look the **same**?

More support Use your software to play the 'My family' listening game.

My toys

 **Listen** → Listen to the new words. The first time just listen. The second time, point and say the words. The third time say them more quickly.

 Track 8 CD 2

Listen, point and say!

Listen, stick, say!

I like .... (cars/trains/dolls).

  Speaking & listening   Try finding toys in your classroom or at home. Say your favourite toys. 'I like ...'.

Sing

Listen to the song first, then join in by pointing to or holding up toys you like. Finally try singing the whole song together.

Track 9
CD 2

Software includes animated songs!

Sing and move!

I like toys. I like toys.
Toys are for girls and boys.

I like trains and balls and cars,
magic wands and twinkly stars.

I like toys. I like toys.
Toys are for girls and boys.

I like soft and cuddly things,
computer games and fairy wings.

Oral fluency

Children develop their communication skills by listening and singing along to songs.

15

Listen

Listen to the sound at the start of each toy.
Match the Letterlander to the toy that starts with their sound.

Track 10
CD 2

Listen and match!

More support

Use your software to play the 'My toys' listening game.

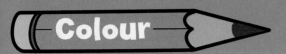 **Colour**

Colour six toys!

Circle Circle the odd one out!

Can you find five differences between these two pictures?

18

Answer: balloon colour changed; number on tricycle disappeared; train track disappeared; teddy colour changed; hat on Talking Tess.

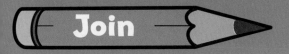

Join the dots to finish the picture.

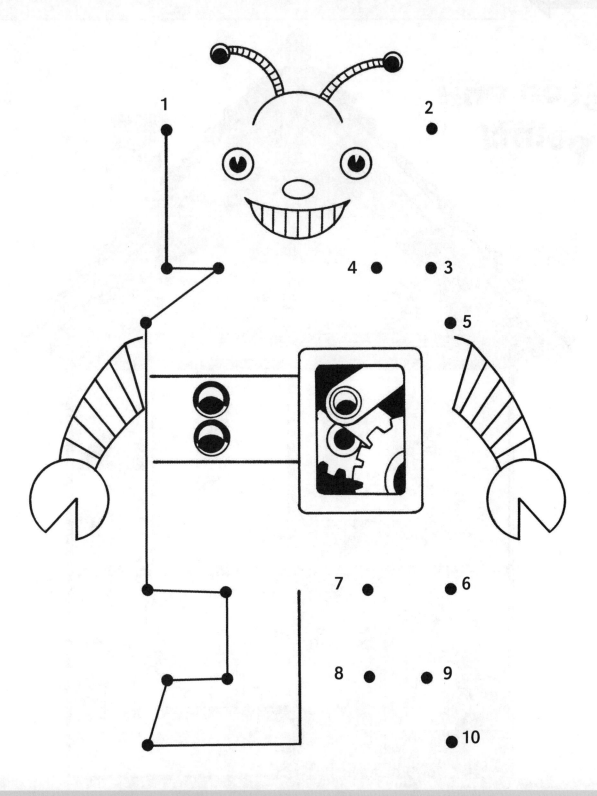

My house

Track 11 CD 2

Listen — Listen to the new words. Point to the rooms within the house.

Listen and point!

Speaking & listening

This exercise improves listening and comprehension skills so children can start to identify words quickly.

Sing

Listen to the song first, then join in with actions of taking off shoes and pointing to the rooms. Finally try singing the song together.

Track 12
CD 2

Software includes animated songs!

Sing and point!

This is my house, welcome inside.

Take off your shoes. I'll be your guide.

A kitchen, a bathroom, a sitting room,

an office, a hallway and bedrooms, too.

This is my house, welcome inside. (x2)

This is my house, welcome inside.

Oral fluency Children develop their communication skills by listening and singing along to songs. Try drawing your own house, too!

21

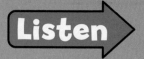 **Listen**

Listen to the names of the rooms in order. Put the correct sticker in the space provided. Then try saying the names of all the rooms.

Track 13
CD 2

 # Listen and stick!

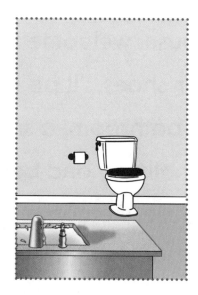

More support Use your software to play the 'My house' listening game.

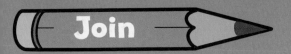
Join the matching pairs of houses. Circle the odd one out.

Join the Letterlanders to their houses!

Letter sounds and actions!

The aim of this section is simply to **start** to familarise children with the Letterlanders and letter sounds using lots of multi-sensory actions. All letter shapes and sounds will be revisited in greater depth in *Fix-it Phonics Level 1*. Just have fun singing the songs and chants!

Sing ➡️ Sing and join in with the Actions Song!

Track 14
CD 2

Sing and move!

Now it's time to do actions.
Now it's time to learn letter sounds.
Now it's time to do actions.
Stand up, and turn around! x2

Yeah!

 Oral fluency

Children develop their communication skills by listening and singing along to songs.

25

Listen Meet Sammy Snake. Say his sound. Then spot him in the scene.

Track 15
CD 2

Sammy Snake says, **S**.

Spot him in school!

Track 16
CD 2

Action!

Listen to the chant and join in with the action by making snake movements with your hand and arm.

Move and chant!

Sss, sss, sss.
Sammy Snake! (x 2)

Software includes animated chants!

Discuss Talk about what you can see in the scene. You can use your native language. Encourage discussion and exploration. Compare your school/class.

Sammy Snake

Colour Sammy Snake and the objects that start with his sound.

Search and stick! Add Sammy Snake's Action Sticker.

Track 17
CD 2

Annie Apple says, **a**.

Spot her in school!

Track 18
CD 2

Move and chant!

A, a, a, a, a.

Annie Apple! (x 2)

Multi-sensory

Linking an action with a sound provides a multi-sensory recall route.

Colour Annie Apple and all the apples!

Search and stick! Add Annie Apple's Action Sticker.

Track 19
CD 2

Talking Tess says, **t**.

Spot her in school!

Action!

Listen to the chant and join in with the action by sticking your arms out in a '**t**' shape.

Track 20
CD 2

Move and chant!

T, t, t.
Talking Tess! (x 2)

Discuss Talk about what you can see in the scene. You can use your native language. Encourage discussion and exploration. Compare your school/class.

Talking Tess

Colour Talking Tess and the objects that start with her sound.

Search and stick! Add Talking Tess's Action Sticker.

31

Track 21
CD 2

Peter Puppy says, **p**.

Spot him in school!

Action!

Listen to the chant and join in with the action by stroking down imaginary long ears.

Track 22
CD 2

Move and chant!

P, p, p, p, p, p.
Peter Puppy! (x 2)

Multi-sensory   Linking an action with a sound provides a multi-sensory recall route.

Peter Puppy

Colour Peter Puppy and the objects that start with his sound.

Search and stick! Add Peter Puppy's Action Sticker.

Listen
Listen to Impy Ink's sound. Then spot him in the scene.

Track 23
CD 2

Impy Ink says, **i**. He says, i in insect.

How many insects can you see?

Incredible Insects

Big Book of Insects

Use your stickers!

Track 24

Action!

Listen to the chant and join in with the action rubbing fingers as if sticky with ink, making an 'icky' face.

Move and chant!

I, i, i, i, i, i.
Impy Ink! (x 2)

Discuss — Talk about what you can see in this scene.
Use your stickers to put the correct number in the box.

Colour Impy Ink and the objects that start with his sound.

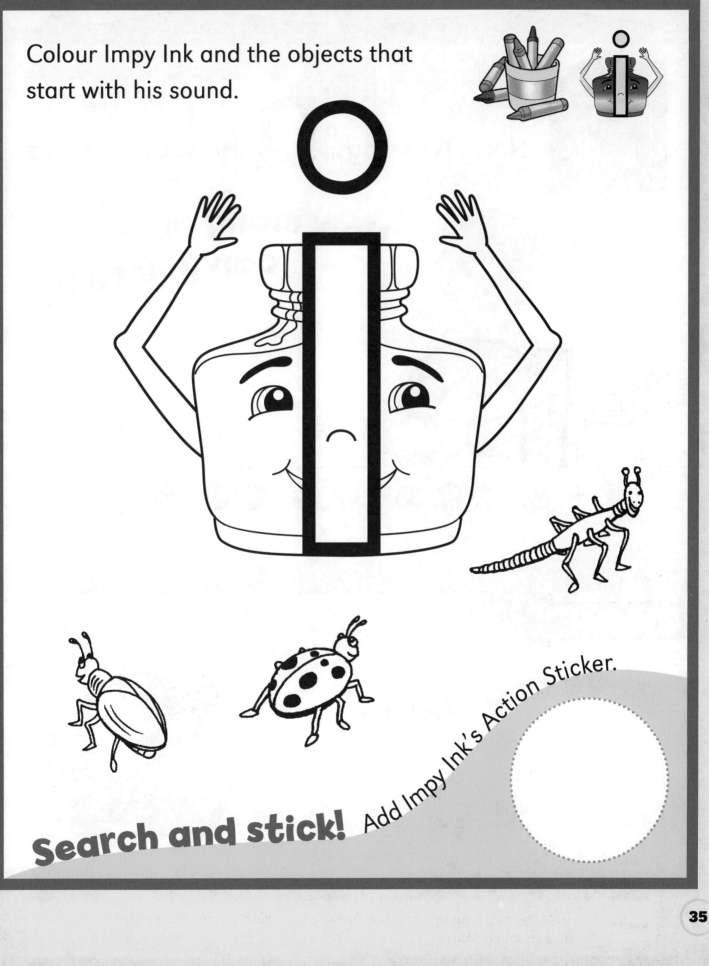

Search and stick! Add Impy Ink's Action Sticker.

Track 25
CD 2

Noisy Nick says, **n**. He says, n in nuts.

How many nuts can you see?

Use your stickers!

Action!

Listen to the chant and join in with the action by banging one fist on top of the other, as if hammering in a nail.

Track 26

Move and chant!

Nnn, nnn,
Noisy Nick! (x 2)

Review Take the opportunity to review previous learning on noises, numbers and counting skills.

Colour Noisy Nick and the objects that start with his sound.

Search and stick! Add Noisy Nick's Action Sticker.

Listen
Listen to Munching Mike's sound and spot all the mice!

Track 27
CD 2

Munching Mike says, **m**.

He says, m in mice.

How many mice can you see?

Use your stickers!

Action!

Listen to the chant and join in with the action by rubbing your tummy and saying '**mmm**'.

Track 28

Move and chant!

Mmm, mmm.
Munching Mike! (x 2)

Review
Take the opportunity to review previous learning on animal sounds and numbers.

Munching Mike

Colour Munching Mike
and the object that
starts with his sound.

MILK

Search and stick! Add Munching Mike's Action Sticker.

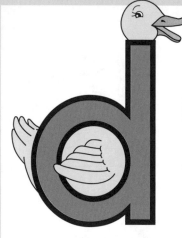

Dippy Duck says, **d**.

She says, d in dog.

How many dogs can you see?

Use your stickers!

Action! Listen to the chant and join in with the action by waddling and flapping your arms like a duck.

Track 30
CD 2

Move and chant!

D, d, d, d, d.
Dippy Duck! (x 2)

Multi-sensory Linking an action with a sound provides a multi-sensory recall route.

Dippy Duck

Colour Dippy Duck and the animal that starts with her sound.

Search and stick! Add Dippy Duck's Action Sticker.

Track 31
CD 2

Golden Girl says, **g**.

She says, g in goat.

It's Golden Girl's granny!

Action!

Listen to the chant and join in with the action glugging a drink.

Track 32
CD 2

Move and chant!

G, g, g, g.
Golden Girl! (x 2)

Discuss & draw

Encourage discussion and exploration. Review previous learning on family members. Now draw a picture of your grandma.

Golden Girl

Colour Golden Girl and the animal that starts with her sound.

Search and stick! Add Golden Girl's Action Sticker.

Track 33
CD 2

Oscar Orange says, O.

He says, o in on.

ON
OFF

Action!

Listen to the chant and join in with the action by making an 'o' shape with your hand and mouth.

Track 34
CD 2

Move and chant!

O, o, o, o, o,
Oscar Orange! (x 2)

Discuss & draw

Encourage discussion and exploration. Review previous learning on family members. Now draw a picture of your own brother or sister.

Oscar Orange

Colour Oscar Orange and draw something for him to sit on!

Search and stick! Add Oscar Orange's Action Sticker.

Listen Listen to Clever Cat's sound and count the cats in the scene.

Track 35
CD 2

Clever Cat says, **C**. She says, c in cat.

Count how many cats!

Use your stickers!

Action!

Listen to the chant and join in with the action by stroking your cheeks like cat's whiskers.

Track 36
CD 2

Move and chant!

C, c, Clever Cat! (x 4)

Multi-sensory Linking an action with a sound provides a multi-sensory recall route.

Clever Cat

Colour Clever Cat and the things that start with her sound.

Search and stick! Add Clever Cat's Action Sticker.

Listen Listen to Kicking King's sound. Trace the path of the ball!

Track 37
CD 2

k

Kicking King says, **k**.

He says, k in kick.

Finger trace

Kicking King kicks!

Action! Listen to the chant and join in with the action by raising your leg and arm to make a 'k' shape.

Track 38
CD 2

Move and chant!

K, k, k.
Kicking King! (x 2)

 Finger-trace Improve hand-eye coordination by encouraging children to use their fingers to trace over lines. This increases confidence prior to using pencils for writing.

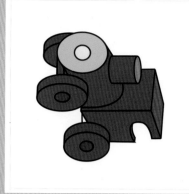

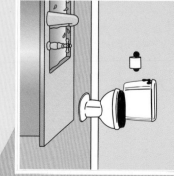

Listen and stick! – How many?

Pages 34, 36, 38, 40

5

5

9

7

Listen and stick! – Harry Hat Man's horse

Page 56

Fix-it Phonics Starter – Activity Book 2

9 9 5 7

Listen and stick! - Can you find them?

Pages 68, 70, 72, 74, 76

Reward stickers

I know my
alphabet sounds!

L e t t e r l a n d

Fix-it Phonics

Kicking King

Colour Kicking King and the object that starts with his sound.

Search and stick! Add Kicking King's Action Sticker.

Track 39
CD 2

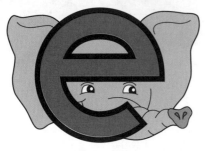

Eddy Elephant says, **e**.

He says, e in egg.

How many eggs can you see?

Use your stickers!

Action! → Listen to the chant and join in with the action by flapping your hands like elephant ears.

Track 40
CD 2

Move and chant!

E, e, e. E, e, e.
Eddy Elephant! (x 2)

50

Multi-sensory Linking an action with a sound provides a multi-sensory recall route.

Colour Eddy Elephant and the things that start with his sound.

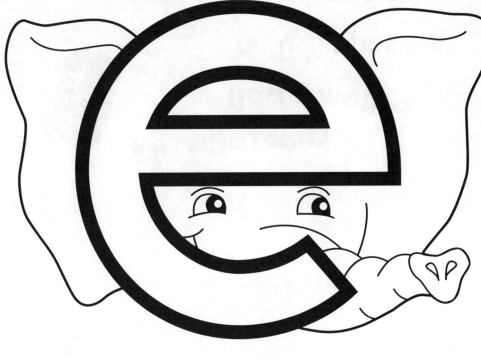

Search and stick! Add Eddy Elephant's Action Sticker.

Track 41
CD 2

Uppy Umbrella says, **U**.

She says, u in up.

Follow Uppy Umbrella up!

Finger trace

Action!

Listen to the chant and join in with the action by pretending to put an umbrella up.

Track 42
CD 2

Move and chant!

U, u, u. U, u, u.
Uppy Umbrella! (x 2)

52 Multi-sensory

Linking an action with a sound provides a multi-sensory recall route.

Uppy Umbrella

Colour Uppy Umbrella and the objects that start with her sound.

Search and stick! Add Uppy Umbrella's Action Sticker.

Listen
Listen to Red Robot's sound then count the red toys.

Track 43
CD 2

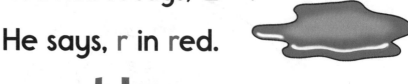

Red Robot says, **r**.

He says, r in red.

Count how many toys are red!

Use your stickers!

Action!

Listen to the chant and join in with the action by making a running movement with your arms while growling.

Track 44
CD 2

Move and chant!

Rrr, rrr,
Red Robot! (x 2)

Discuss & review
Talk about what you can see in the scene. Remind children of the names of some of the toys and review previous learning on toys and colours.

Red Robot

Colour Red Robot and circle his favourite colour.

Search and stick! Add Red Robot's Action Sticker.

Harry Hat Man says, **h**.

He says, h in hat.

hay

Move and chant!

Hhh, hhh, hhh.
Harry Hat Man! (x 2)

Stickers Talk about what you can see in the scene. Review previous learning on animals. Stick a hat on Harry Hat Man's horse.

Harry Hat Man

Colour Harry Hat Man and the objects
that start with his sound.

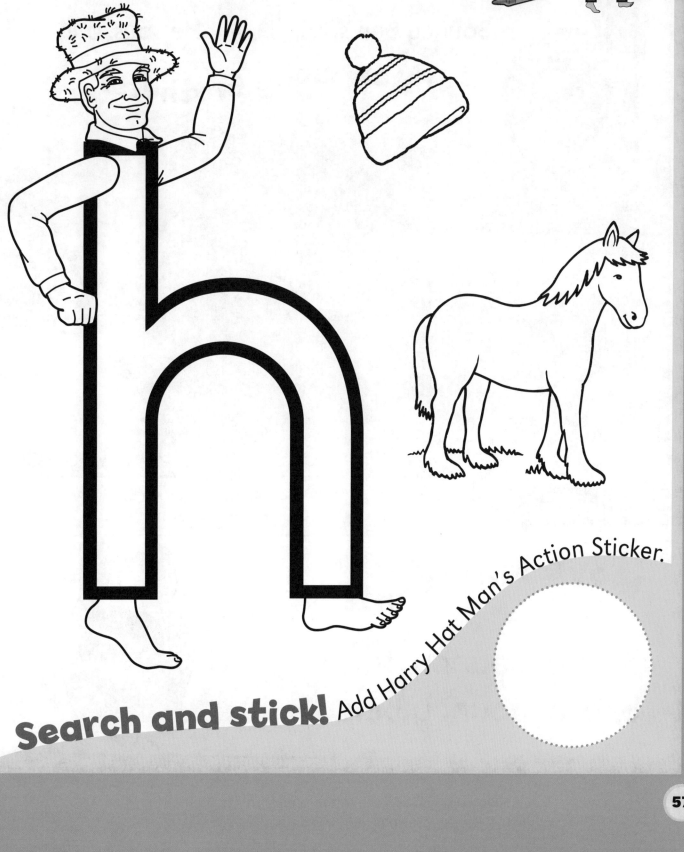

Search and stick! Add Harry Hat Man's Action Sticker.

Track 47
CD 2

Bouncy Ben says, **b**. He says, b in bed.

How many brothers?

Use your stickers!

Action! Listen to the chant and join in with the action by shooting your arms up for ears and wiggling them.

Track 48
CD 2

Move and chant!

B, b, b. Bouncy Ben!
B, b, b. Bouncy Ben!

Discuss & review Talk about what you can see in the scene. This is Bouncy Ben's home - a burrow. Review previous learning on houses/rooms.

Bouncy Ben

Colour Bouncy Ben and the objects that start with his sound.

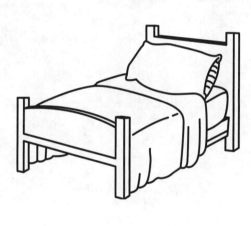

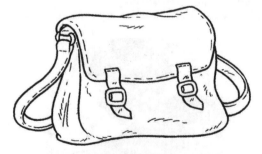

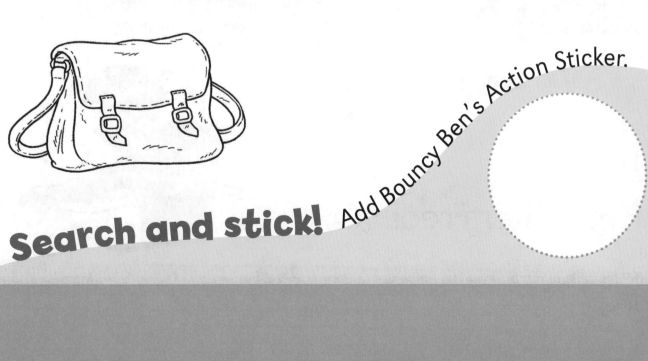

Search and stick! Add Bouncy Ben's Action Sticker.

Firefighter Fred says, **f**.

He says, f in farm.

Find Firefighter Fred!

Action!

Listen to the chant and join in with the action holding and pointing an imaginary hose towards an imaginary fire.

Track 50
CD 2

Move and chant!

Fff, fff.

Firefighter Fred! (x 2)

Pair work
Take the opportunity to review previous learning on animal sounds and the alliterative numbers 4 and 5.

Firefighter Fred

Colour Firefighter Fred and the numbers that start with his sound.

4

5

Search and stick! Add Firefighter Fred's Action Sticker.

Track 51
CD 2

Lucy Lamp Light says **l**. She says, l in leg.

Look for Lucy!

Listen to the chant and join in with the action by touching your fingers above your head to suggest Lucy's hat.

Track 52
CD 2

Move and chant!

Lll, lll.
Lucy Lamp Light! (x 2)

62

Discuss Talk about what you can see in the scene. Encourage discussion and exploration. Compare your village/town/city. Review learning on body parts.

Lucy Lamp Light

Colour Lucy Lamp Light and the thing that starts with her sound.

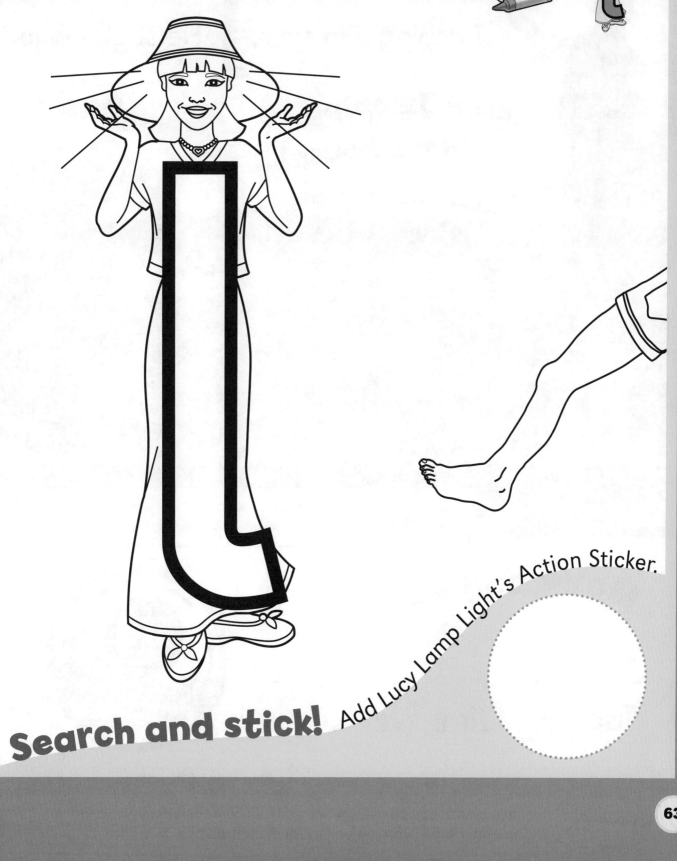

Search and stick! Add Lucy Lamp Light's Action Sticker.

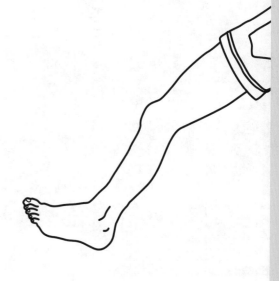

Track 53
CD 2

Jumping Jim says, **j**. He says, j in jet.

Find Jumping Jim's house!

Track 54
CD 2

Action!

Listen to the chant and join in with the action by pretending you are juggling an imaginary set of balls.

Move and chant!

J, j, j. J, j, j.
Jumping Jim! (x 2)

64 **Discuss** Talk about what you can see in the scene. Encourage discussion and exploration. Review learning on environmental sounds.

Colour Jumping Jim and the object that
begins with his sound.

Search and stick! Add Jumping Jim's Action Sticker.

Track 55
CD 2

Vicky Violet says, **V**.

She says, v in vet.

Action!

Listen to the chant and join in with the action by holding both hands up and outwards to form a 'v' shape.

Track 56
CD 2

Move and chant!

Vvv, vvv.
Vicky Violet! (x 2)

Look & discuss Listen to Vicky Violet and say her sound. Look at the picture of the vet. The vet is Vicky Violet's mum. Review previous learning on family members.

Colour Vicky Violet and the object that starts with her sound. Follow the line with your pencil.

Search and stick!

Add Vicky Violet's Action Sticker.

Walter Walrus says, **W**.

He says, w in wind.

Where is Walter?

Action! Listen to the chant and join in with the action by flicking both hands up and outwards so your arms form a 'w' shape.

Track 58
CD 2

Move and chant!

Www, www.

Walter Walrus! (x 2)

Discuss & Stick! Talk about what you can see in the scene. Encourage discussion and exploration.

Found Walter Walrus?

Add a star sticker!

Walter Walrus

Colour Walter Walrus and then follow the wavy line with your pencil.

Search and stick!

Add Walter Walrus's Action Sticker.

Listen Listen to Fix-it Max. Say his sound, then look for him!

Track 59
CD 2

Fix-it Max says, **X**.

He says, x in six.

6

Find Fix-it Max!

Action!

Listen to the chant and join in with the action by crossing your arms on your chest to make an 'x' shape.

Track 60
CD 2

Move and chant!

X, x, x.

Fix-it Max! (x 2)

Discuss & Stick! Talk about what you can see in the scene. Encourage discussion and exploration.

Found Fix-it Max? Add a star sticker!

Colour Fix-it Max and the number that **ends** with his sound.

Search and stick! Add Fix-it Max's Action Sticker.

Listen Meet Yellow Yo-yo Man. Say his sound, then look for him!

Track 61
CD 2

Yellow Yo-yo Man says, **y**.

He says, y in yellow.

Where is Yellow Yo-yo Man?

Action!

Listen to the chant and join in with the action by moving your hand up and down as if playing with a yo-yo.

Track 62
CD 2

Move and chant!

Y, y, y, y.
Yellow Yo-yo Man! (x 2)

72

Discuss & Stick!

Talk about what you can see in the scene. Encourage discussion and exploration.

Found Yellow Yo-yo Man?

Add a star sticker!

Yellow Yo-yo Man

Colour Yellow Yo-yo Man and count the yellow yo-yos!

Search and stick! Add Yellow Yo-yo Man's Action Sticker.

Track 63
CD 2

Zig Zag Zebra says, **Z**.

She says, z in zip.

Look for Zig Zag Zebra!

Action!

Listen to the chant and join in with the action by resting your head against your hands to mime falling asleep.

Track 64
CD 2

Move and chant!

Zzz, zzz,
Zig Zag Zebra! (x 2)

Discuss & Stick!

Talk about what you can see in the scene. Encourage discussion and exploration.

Found Zig Zag Zebra?
Add a star sticker!

Zig Zag Zebra

Colour Zig Zag Zebra and the things that start with her sound.

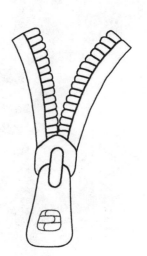

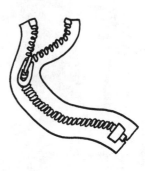

Search and stick! Add Zig Zag Zebra's Action Sticker.

Listen
Meet Quarrelsome Queen. Say her sound, then look for her!

Track 65
CD 2

Quarrelsome Queen says, **q**.

She says, q in quiet.

Find the Queen!

Action!

Listen to the chant and join in with the action by pointing your index finger as if asking for 'Quiet!'.

Track 66
CD 2

Move and chant!

Qu, qu, qu, qu.

Quarrelsome Queen! (x 2)

Discuss & Stick!

Talk about what you can see in the scene. Encourage discussion and exploration.

Found Quarrelsome Queen?
Add a star sticker!

Colour Quarrelsome Queen and the person
that starts with her sound.

Search and stick! Add Quarrelsome Queen's Action Sticker.

Match the Letterlanders to their black letter shapes.

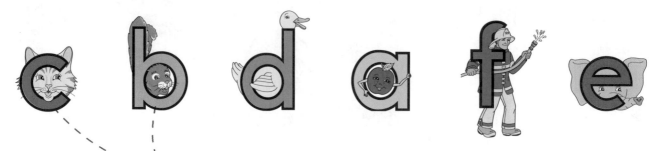

a b c d e f

g h i j k l

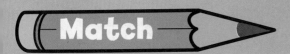

m n o p q r s

t u v w x y z

Blend ➜ Let's try and blend sounds together. Think of your arm as a slide with the sounds attached. Slide down to blend the sounds.

Track 67
CD 2

It is important for children to start to see words as being made up of separate phonemes. This technique allows them to 'see' and 'feel' the sounds as they blend together to make the words.

Sound slide!

on

Oral blending This technique helps children imagine the sounds in order. Say the individual sounds first, then move faster down your arm slide to blend the sounds!

Blend

Gradually introduce more words. Use only 1-syllable words and make sure that they are easily 'sounded out'.

Track 68
CD 2

Sound slide!

dad

dad

Sound slide!

Track 69
CD 2

hat

Track 70
CD 2

cat

cat

 Oral blending These two words end in the same way. Show that by just changing one letter at the start the new word is formed.

When '**c**' and '**k**' are together they make just one sound. Listen to the sound slide for the word 'kick'. Blend the sounds on your arm.

Track 71
CD 2

Sound slide!

k
i
ck

We both make the same sound. We often sit together at the end of words.

kick

kick ➜

More words to 'Sound slide' include:	bed	nut	six
	jet	pen	sun
	leg	red	zip

Oral blending

NOTE: Only start to try and blend sounds together if you feel your class is ready. At this stage it does not matter if children are unable to blend or segment the sounds themselves. All letter sounds are introduced in greater detail and blending techniques are consolidated in *Fix-it Phonics Level 1*.

Action Song ➤ Listen to the song and join in with the actions. As you listen for the second and third times, try and join in!

Track 72
CD 2

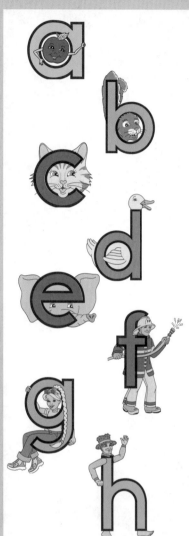

Annie Apple says,

Bouncy Ben says,

Clever Cat says,

Dippy Duck says,

Eddy Elephant says,

Firefighter Fred says,

Golden Girl says,

Harry Hat Man says,

a
b
c
d
e
f
g
h

We all know our letter sounds. We love Letterland!

Impy Ink says,

Jumping Jim says,

Kicking King says,

i
j
k

Multi-sensory Linking an action with a sound provides a multi-sensory recall route.

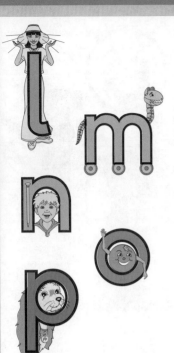

Lucy Lamp Light says,

Munching Mike says,

Noisy Nick says,

Oscar Orange says,

Peter Puppy says,

We all know our letter sounds. We love Letterland!

Quarrelsome Queen says,

Red Robot says,

Sammy Snake says,

Talking Tess says,

Uppy Umbrella says,

Vicky Violet says,

Walter Walrus says,

Fix-it Max says,

Yellow Yo-yo Man says,

Zig Zag Zebra says,

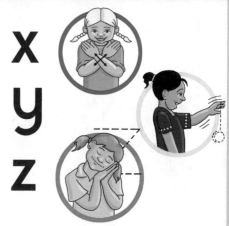

We all know our letter sounds. We love Letterland!

a b c d e f g h i j k l m

n o p q r s t u v w x y z

Then there are the Vowel Men, who like to say their names.

Mr A says, **a**

Mr E says, **e**

Mr I says, **i**

Mr O says, **o**

Mr U says, **u**. That's just what they do!

We all know our letter sounds. We love Letterland!

Yes! We all know our letter sounds.

We love Letterland!

Software includes animated song!

Multi-sensory

Linking an action with a sound provides a multi-sensory recall route.

Letterland

Certificate!

Fix-it Phonics Complete

This is to certify that

....

has finished

LETTERLAND® Fix-it Phonics Starter

Signed: ....

Your Letterland teacher

Date: ....

www.letterland.com

Annie Apple   Bouncy Ben   Clever Cat   Dippy Duck   Eddy Elephant   Firefighter Fred

Golden Girl   Harry Hat Man   Impy Ink   Jumping Jim   Kicking King   Lucy Lamp Light

Munching Mike   Noisy Nick   Oscar Orange   Peter Puppy   Quarrelsome Queen   Red Robot   Sammy Snake

Talking Tess   Uppy Umbrella   Vicky Violet   Walter Walrus   Fix-it Max   Yellow Yo-yo Man   Zig Zag Zebra

Well done! See you again soon!